LETTERLAND
In the Town
Sticker Book

Devised by
Richard Carlisle and Jane Launchbury
Written, designed and illustrated by
Jane Launchbury
With consultant advice from
Lyn Wendon,
originator of Letterland

Contents

You might like to add some of the extra stickers to this page.

This Sticker Book
belongs to

_____

_____

At the Shops

Complete the colouring and add the stickers.
Then draw a line from each shop to something that is sold there.

Can you count the cakes?

Finish Sammy Snake.

Butcher **Videos**

Bookshop

video

Bouncy Ben has been to the shops.
Look in his basket and point to the shops that he has visited.

Greengrocer

Book of Bedtime Stories

Around the Town

A game for up to 4 players.
1. Make counters by sticking character stickers on pieces of thin card. Choose 1 each.
2. Place all counters on START.

3. Throw a dice in turn. The highest scorer goes first, the lowest last.
4. Take turns to throw the dice and move around the town.
5. The first to reach the town centre is the winner.

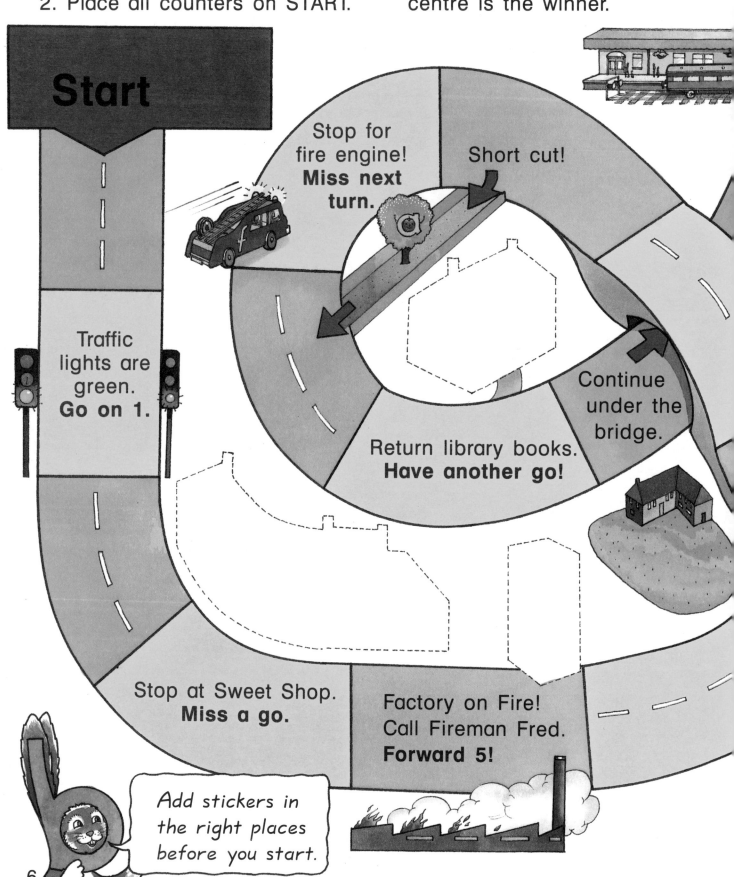

Start

Stop for fire engine! **Miss next turn.**

Short cut!

Traffic lights are green. **Go on 1.**

Continue under the bridge.

Return library books. **Have another go!**

Stop at Sweet Shop. **Miss a go.**

Factory on Fire! Call Fireman Fred. **Forward 5!**

Add stickers in the right places before you start.

6

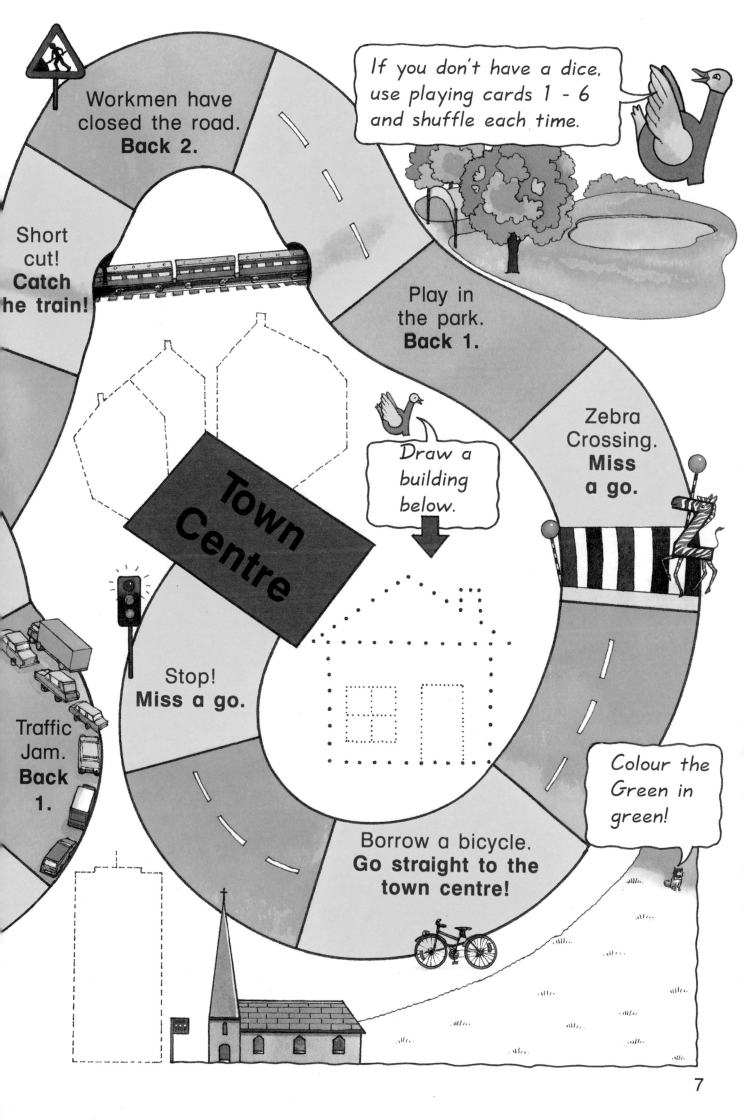

At the Market

Colour the big apples below. Count them and put the right number sticker with them and the vowel man sticker above.

How many ice creams can you colour? Add the right number sticker and a sign to help Mr I sell more ice creams.

In the Park

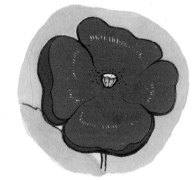
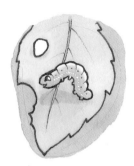

Munching Mike's Mystery

mirror

Medieval Map

moon

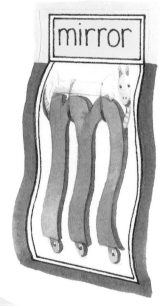

moth

millipede

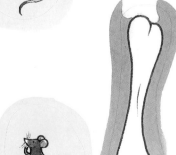

 moss

Going to Town

At the Market

Get your
ice
cream
here!

Around the Town

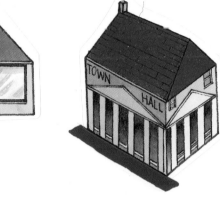

At the Shops

Fish & Chips

Shoe Shop

Toyshop

   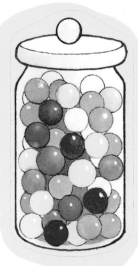

Spot the Differences

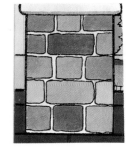

Map Maze

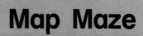

Extra Stickers

To use as you choose.

Cats will sleep anywhere.

Get your yo-yos here!

What is this man selling? Colour his letter yellow and load his backpack. Join the dots. Colour and count the big yo-yos.

Colour the orange and add the last number and vowel man sticker.
Now add the last few stickers .

Did you find 5 other mice in the market?

9

In the Park

Poor Peter has gone to play in the park. Finish colouring the picture then put the stickers on.
Who can you see?
What are they doing?

Spot the Differences

Things are always changing in towns.
There are 10 differences that you can
put right by using stickers.

Can you spot
3 other tiny
differences?

Map Maze

Use your finger to show Golden Girl how to get through the town to buy some flowers and take them to her Granny.

STOP

13

Munching Mike's Mystery

1. Munching Mike has a mystery to solve. He has found a massive monster bone on Misty Mountain! The mystery is - where did it come from?
His Mum has sent him to the Letterland Museum to show the bone to the museum keeper.
But Mike is in a mighty muddle. "This museum is like a maze. I need a map!" he mumbles.

Add the big bone here.

Can you help Munching Mike find his way through the museum? Add some mice in the rooms. How many mice will Mike meet?

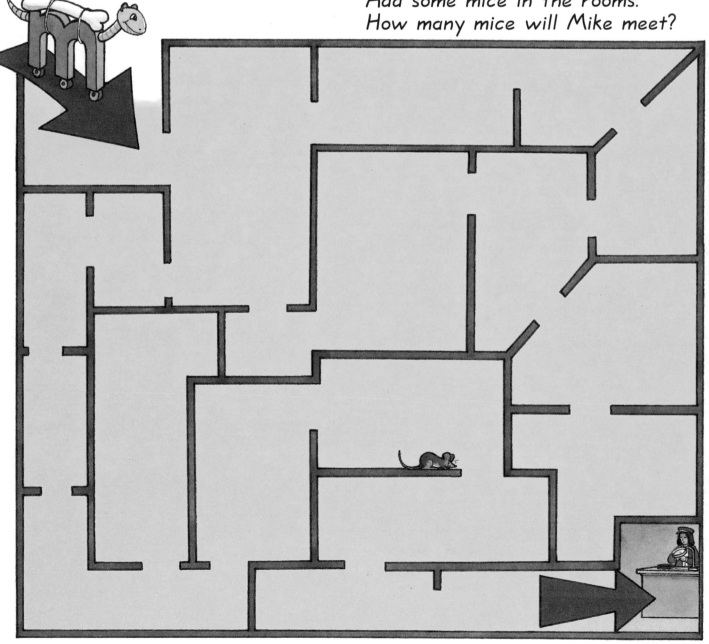

2. At last! Munching Mike meets the museum keeper.
"My, my," she says. "I think you've found my missing mammoth bone! Follow me."

3. This time Munching Mike is not lost, so he looks around. When they go through the History Room he sees plenty he'd like to munch. But a man says "Don't touch!".

4. "Mmm," says Munching Mike in the Natural History room. "Moss and a moth for my lunch." But the Museum Keeper rushes him on to the Science room.

5. "A magnet - my favourite food!" says Mike. Then he sees a metal monster, just like himself but taller and bendier! He thinks it must be a magic mirror.

6. The museum Keeper takes Munching Mike into a big room. In the middle of the floor there is a mighty monster, made up of bones.

7. A monster with a missing leg!

"We call her Mandy the Mammoth," says the museum keeper. She lived a million years ago and these bones are all that is left of her.

Help me add the missing bone.

8. Munching Mike puts the missing bone in place. "Marvellous! A perfect match!" says the museum keeper.

"Now my Mystery is solved", says Munching Mike happily.

Colour Munching Mike.

16